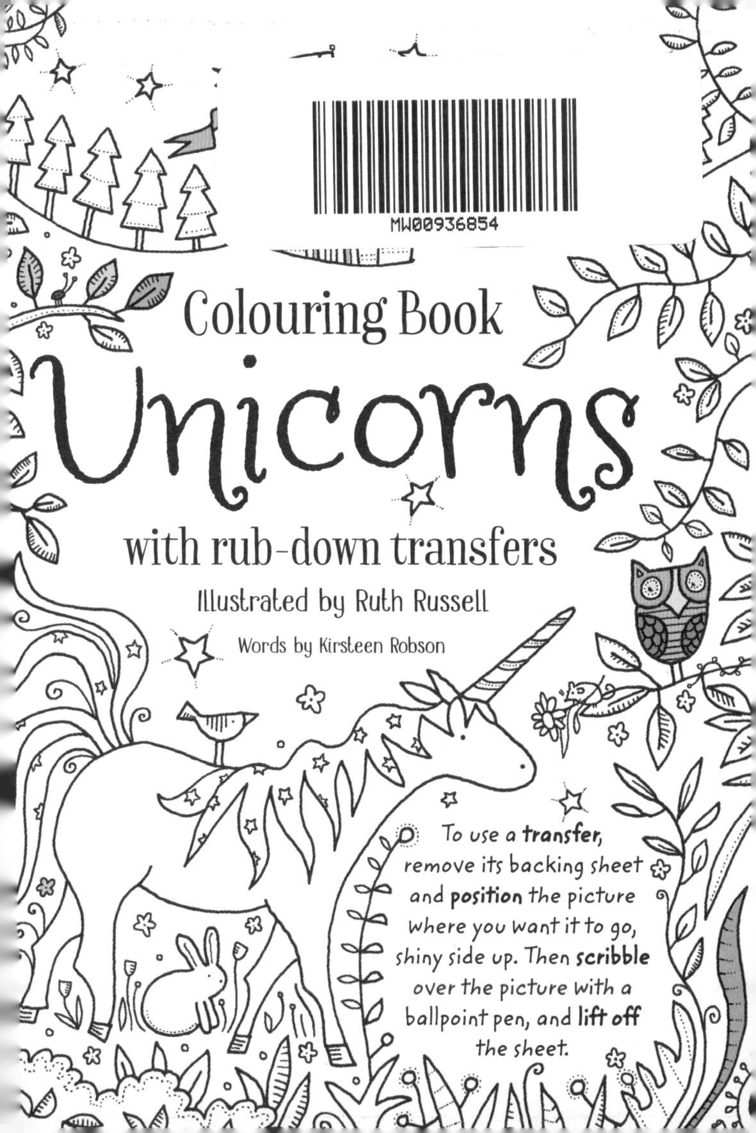

Colouring Book

Unicorns

with rub-down transfers

Illustrated by Ruth Russell

Words by Kirsteen Robson

To use a **transfer**, remove its backing sheet and **position** the picture where you want it to go, shiny side up. Then **scribble** over the picture with a ballpoint pen, and **lift off** the sheet.

In a forest's leafy glade,
unicorns rest on the
cool, green grass.

These unicorns are watching the sparkling stream slipping under the bridge.

Unicorns
love the sweet
smell of ripe
orchard
fruits.

Silver-winged unicorns swoop and soar between the clouds and rainbows.

These unicorns have climbed high into the mountains to see the sun rise.

Unicorns live in the land of dreams and fairytales.

These unicorns are looking at the sea creatures in the clear, shallow water.

A gallop across
snow-cloaked fields
will help keep this
unicorn warm.

The unicorns enjoy watching the wildlife as they bathe in the shady pool.

Little birds fill the air with the songs of Spring.

Hush, little mice!
Don't disturb this
sleeping unicorn.

This royal unicorn stands alone in the pale light of the moon.

First published in 2018 by Usborne Publishing Ltd., Usborne House, 83-85 Saffron Hill, London ECIN 8
England. www.usborne.com Copyright © 2018 Usborne Publishing Ltd. The name Usborne and the devi
are Trade Marks of Usborne Publishing Ltd. All rights reserved. No part of this publication may b
reproduced, stored in a retrieval system or transmitted in any form or by any means, electronic, mechar
photocopying, recording or otherwise without the prior permission of the publisher. UKE. Printed in Cl